Say Again?

Say Again ?

cartoons by VANAN -DEL-

text + design Martin Leeuwis

Distribution: Martin Leeuwis Publications
P.O. Box 192
5250 AD Vlijmen
Holland

A Martin Leeuwis Publication

CIP-GEGEVENS KONINKLIJKE BIBLIOTHEEK, DEN HAAG

Van Andel

Say again? / cartoons by Van Andel; text Martin Leeuwis
Vlijmen: Leeuwis. - illustrated - 1e druk : 1982
ISBN 90-800375-1-6
SISO 659.3 UDC 355.354 (0:741.5)
Trefw.: luchtmacht; cartoons

Aso available by same authors:
"Say no more"
"Say when"
"Say how"

september 1982   first printing
august 1985   2nd printing, minor changes
may 1987   3rd printing
june 1988   4th printing
september 1989   5th printing
july 1990   6th printing
june 1991   7th printing
october 1994   8th printing
september 1998   9th printing, minor changes

Say Again?

A book like this is not something which just happens. Ton has been drawing cartoons for many years and Martin has been collecting funny stories since he joined 314 Squadron. We both had (independently) been thinking about a book, but there is a large distance between thinking and doing. We met eachother and things started moving as we decided to start working together. The year 1982 has been "the year of the book" for us, but we thought it was worth the effort. And it was, as orders started flooding in from allover the world. Numerous reviews appeared in aviation magazines and they had one thing in common: enthousiasm. This enthousiasm resulted in a much earlier reprint than we had considered possible. There were also some small differences between the first and second edition, but basically the books are the same.
We are allready considering our next book, but don't become to hopefull, it will take a while.
Finally we hope you like this book, but please don't follow the text to the letter. ATC will never forgive us when everybody answers "again" to the question "say again?"

Ton van Andel   Martin Leeuwis

Flying is still a very young science. Even my grandmother is older than flying history, which started at Kill Devil Hill, Kitty Hawk, USA, on the 17th of December 1903 when the Wright brothers made a powered flight of 120 feet. The wingspan of today's aircraft is even larger than this first hop, but still it was a great hop forward for mankind.

As happens with every new invention, it was not greeted enthousiastically by everybody. Many people had never seen anything more complicated than a bicycle, and for them flying was just impossible. Of course aircraft of those days did not look very trustworthy with their clattering, oil spewing and seizing engines and wood and linen rackety constructions.

Flying was reserved for daredevils.

YES, I KNOW YOU ARE AN EXPERT
YACHTSMAN, BUT THERE ARE SOME
DIFFERENCES FROM SAILING, YOU KNOW.

For our grandparents flying was a very strange and new thing; for us it is almost as normal as walking. Intercontinental travel and short holidays abroad became possible with aviation. But do you realize that next to the invention of flying itself, they had to invent all those other small and necessary bits and pieces.

WHY DON'T WE CHOCK THE WHEELS ?

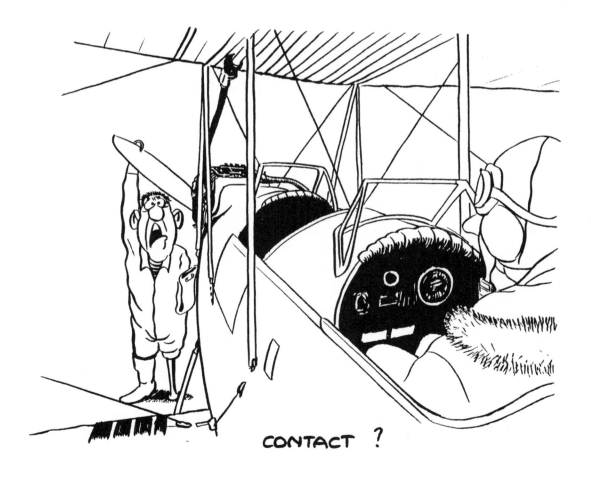

CONTACT ?

Snappy answers dept 1

Tower: *Redskin Green, this is the tower, say fuelstate!*
Pilot: *Fuelstate.*
Tower: *Say again!*
Pilot: *Again*
Tower says nothing anymore and goes downstairs to drink a cup of coffee.

This is what we call

LOW LEVEL NAVIGATION

A MISSED APPROACH

A fighter pilot was transferred from one squadron to another. The distance between his old and new unit was quite large, so he decided to buy another house, close to his new unit. After a while he found a really nice house, in a beautiful and quiet neighbourhood. The owner did not want to bargain about the price because he expected many more potential buyers in the following weeks. During those weeks he and a few helpful colleagues started every navigation, gunnery range, instrument and formation flight with a leaving procedure which brought them right over this house. The pilot later returned to the owner, and bought the house, at a bargain.

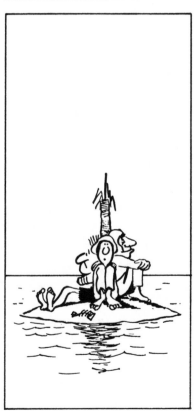

The nose of the Jumbo was damaged when the captain taxied it right into the departure building. He was returning from the runway threshold after deciding not to take off because he suspected the brakes.

You were right about those brakes, captain!

LADIES AND GENTLEMEN, WE JUST DISCOVERED
AN EXCEPTION TO THE RULE THAT WHAT
GOES UP MUST COME DOWN : THE LANDING GEAR

LOW-COST AIRLINE, I SUPPOSE

Flying a military jet properly means more than making a safe take-off and a smooth landing. It takes the pilots years to learn the art of tactical flying, which is based upon an element of two aircraft. The aim of this two-ship is to share the workload and to double the effectiveness. The main things you want are the covering of each others tail and the dividing of lookout sectors during normal flight and the information about threats to the engaged fighter. during the attack phase. The first rules in the book about tactical formation flying were written down by German aces in World War One. It took the rest of the world a while to learn about: "check for the high Hun in the sun"- "if you see one, start looking for the other"- "check your six, when you are about to make a kill", but they did. Since Word War One the speed range has changed a bit, but one thing hasn't: if an element of two aircraft makes no mistakes, it is hard to get.

This is what we call

A HARD LANDING

A superior pilot may be defined as one who stays out of trouble by using his superior judgement to avoid situations which might require the use of his superior skill.

THEY DON'T NEED US ANYMORE

For many years the Lockheed F104G "Starfighter" had been the backbone of NATO's airpower in Europe. But in the mid-seventies the Starfighter was due for replacement.

The Germans and the Italians had allready made their choice. Together with the British they were going to buy the Panavia Tornado. That was a sophisticated, high-performance, multirole, all-weather, versatile and

rather expensive aircraft.

Other European countries, Norway, Denmark, Belgium and Holland came to the conclusion that the Tornado

exceeded their financial strength.

So these countries started looking around at the aerospace market for a more reasonable price-tagged aircraft. This led up to a deal that was called:

THE SALE OF THE CENTURY

There were 4 rivals on the market; two from Europe and two from the USA. The leading European competitor was Dassault-Breguet of France. Their trumpcard

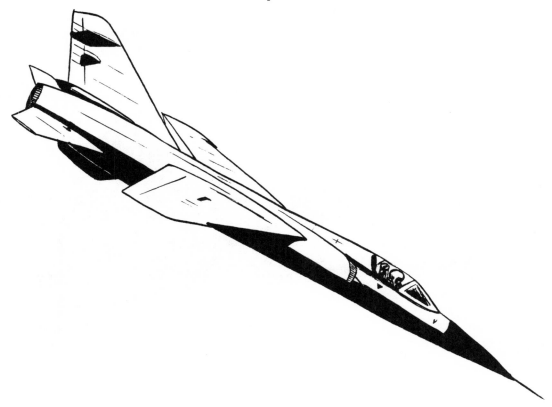

the Mirage F1-E/M53

The other European participator was
Saab-Scania of Sweden. They brought
in the

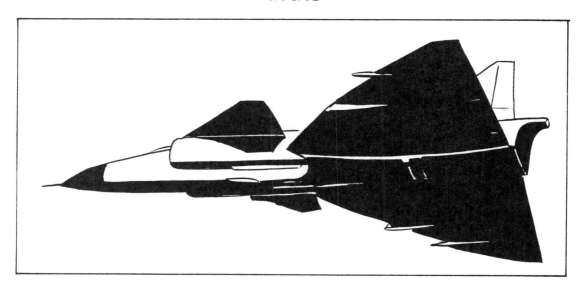

JA-37 Viggen

The United States participated in the competition with two candidates. The first was the Northrop Corporation with the

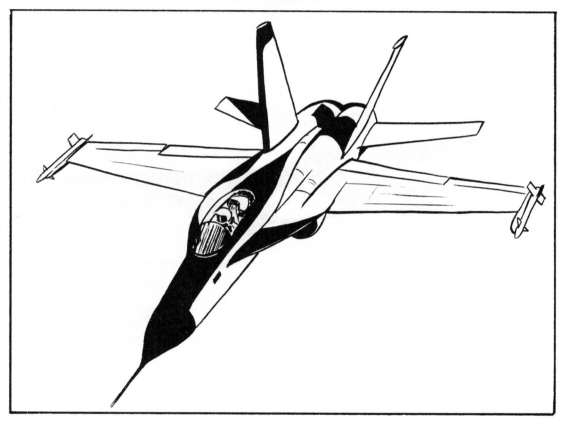

F17 Cobra.

The last of the four rivals was General Dynamics. Their entry was the (by that time nameless)

F16.

At first the four countries had been acting independently and no one was sure they would all end up buying the same aircraft.

*But early in 1974 the four countries
decided they would all purchase the
same aircraft.*

*forming a consortium to negotiate
jointly with the sellers. The winner
would take all.*

That simplified the selection

*since for the Belgians it would be
absolutely alien to agree on a Swedish
aircraft and it would be equally strange
for the Norwegians to buy a French
aircraft.*

So in fact the decision - European or American - was taken, however...

In the USA there remained a problem to be solved. The Europeans were not likely to buy an American aircraft which the USAF itself would not buy in substantial numbers. Initially the USAF showed little interest in either the F16 or the F17. But something was done in the Pentagon resulting in an announcement in June 1974 that the USAF would buy 650 F16's or F17's.

TRENDSETTER FLEET

From that time on, things went fast.
Autumn 1974 the rival fighters showed
their paces in a

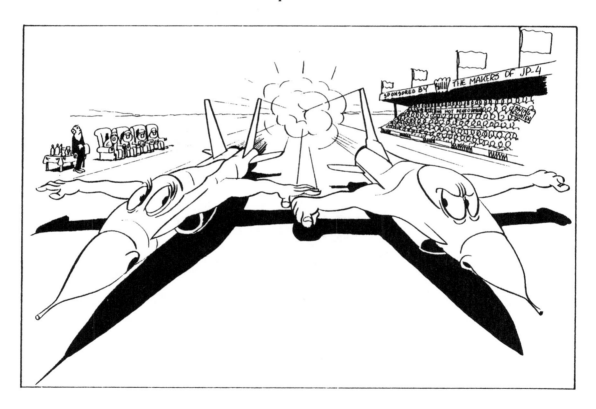

competitive Fly-Off. (to which the
Europeans were thoughtfully invited)

*In January 1975 the Pentagon
announced its choice.*

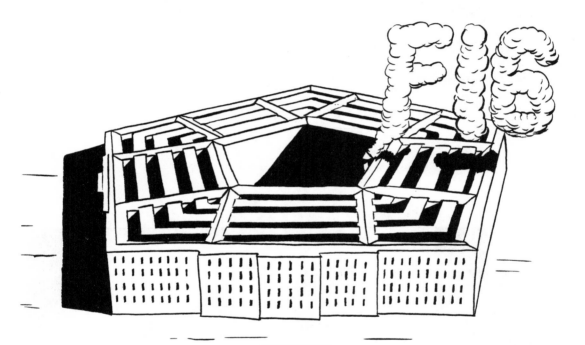

*So it came that in the decennia to come
Norwegian, Danish, Belgian and Dutch
skies are penetrated by the formidable
F16 Fighting Falcon.
We will try to characterize that
remarkable aircraft in some detail at
other pages in this book.*

I WONDER WHERE I LEFT MY SCREWDRIVER . . .

If you do something long enough in a certain way, or if they tell you often enough how to do it, it can be a problem to lose this traditional habit. I'm still putting the garbage outside the door at Wednesday-morning although it should have been Monday-morning for two years now, but eventually I'll learn. Most pilots have a built-in conservatism which makes them fight every change in design or procedure, until they are getting used to the new thing. As they say: it has been working well, so it has to be good.

WHY A CERTAIN PILOTS HABIT DISAPPEARED
WITH THE GLOSTER METEOR

THE WHISKEY FOUR DEMONSTRATION TEAM
WAS AT THE AIRBASE LAST WEEK.

This is what our instructors call

.... AND NEVER FORGET.....

THE 6 P's

PROPER
PREFLIGHT
PLANNING
PREVENTS
POOR
PERFORMANCE

At the 1981 Oshkosh Airshow the following aerobatic routine was flown by Bob Herendeen in his Pitts Special. At least it is what I think he did, because it was quite hard to record:

take off · slow roll · two flick rolls · 1/2 slow roll · outside half loop · 11/2 outside flick roll ·21/2 flick roll · half loop down · 11/4 flick roll to knifeedge · 11/2 flick roll to knife edge ·13/4 roll to inverted · push up to vertical · 4 point turn in stall turn · 4 flick rolls vertical down · pull up for vertical slow roll · tail slide ·flick roll down · loop with three flick rolls in top · knife edge · pull up to lomcevak · inside rolling loop · pull up to vertical · 11/2 flick roll ·stall turn · 11/2 flick roll · pull up to vertical roll · torque rolling tail slide · vertical slow roll down · square loop · 15 turn inverted flat spin ·pull up to vertical slow roll · 4 turn spin · 8 point hesitation roll · 3/4 loop · knife edge ·7/8 loop · 2 flick rolls · landing.

He did this every day, ten days in a row, enjoying himself!

Snappy answers dept 2

Pilot: *Tower, could you give me a rough timecheck?*
Tower: *Today it's Tuesday, Sir.*

I SAY, THIS IS THE MOST PECULIAR ATC
I'VE EVER SEEN

Most people do their daily work because they are used to do it. Pilots are a different kind of workers. When they were schoolboys, they went to the local airfield to watch aeroplanes and they would recognize an aircraft by the sound alone. After dreaming about it for years they had to work hard many years more to get hired and to pass training. As a result the "work" of flying is more or less a hobby. And if something is your hobby, you will talk about it. A group of pilots together will talk about fast cars, women, money and tax but always they will return to the one topic they all know about: FLYING.

...AND THEN I MADE A PITCHBACK IN THE VERTICAL SO THAT....

ROGER

Snappy answers dept 3

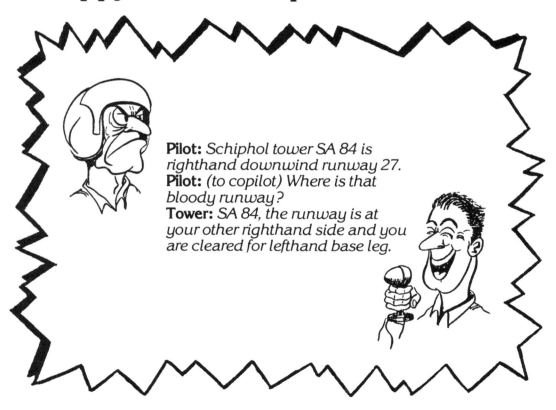

Pilot: *Schiphol tower SA 84 is righthand downwind runway 27.*
Pilot: *(to copilot) Where is that bloody runway?*
Tower: *SA 84, the runway is at your other righthand side and you are cleared for lefthand base leg.*

STOP, THERE'S A BOMB WARNING !

This is what we call

A DRAGCHUTE FAILURE

If you do it long enough, flying becomes a sometimes boring job. In the airlines it consists of getting an aircraft in the air and landing it a few hours later. For normally, nothing special happens. But if it happens, much happens and fast. They call flying a job filled with hours of boredom interspersed with moments of terror. But then, not everybody gets the same treatment. A Dutch Air Force pilot once flew around slowly on an engine check flight when an attacking fighter misjudged it's closing-in speed and hit him. It flew half his wing off and he made a successful ejection at 35.000 feet. A few years later he and a German colleague flying a Fiat G-91 jet did not see eachother and had a head-on collision. They both lost part of their wing and both made a reasonably uneventful landing at the same airfield where they discussed matters. The law of chance says that he can fly around the rest of his life with his eyes closed without hitting another aircraft.
But then, who knows?

STOP TREMBLING, JUST EXPLAIN WHAT HAPPENED

WELL, IT BREAKS
THE ROUTINE

Snappy answers dept 4

Pilot: *Request the present weather?*
Radar: *Ten eights on the deck*
Pilot: *How can you have ten eights?*
Radar: *Well, yesterday we had eight eights and today it's much worse.*

YOU START ON
AN EJECTION SEAT,
YOU FINISH ON
AN OFFICE CHAIR

An Ejection

Leaving your aircraft used to be a difficult procedure. All kinds of tricks were necessary to prevent mutilation of the pilot by a propeller or tail section.
When the jet-age started, the manufactureres invented the ejection seat with an explosive charge to "shoot" the pilot away. Many pilots did not like this design and flew around with safety pins installed. The explosive charge changed into a rocket, which gave a less violent accelleration, and the ejection seat became a trusted way to leave an aircraft in distress.

continued

continued

continued

.... AND HERE WE GO!

OOPS..... I SHOULD HAVE THOUGHT OF THAT....

NOWADAYS THEY PUT THE PARACHUTE IN THE SEAT!

Snappy answers dept 5

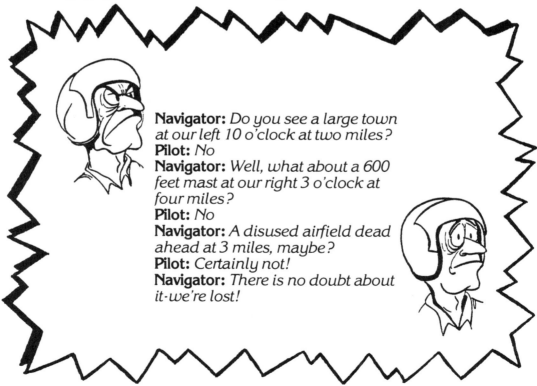

Navigator: *Do you see a large town at our left 10 o'clock at two miles?*
Pilot: *No*
Navigator: *Well, what about a 600 feet mast at our right 3 o'clock at four miles?*
Pilot: *No*
Navigator: *A disused airfield dead ahead at 3 miles, maybe?*
Pilot: *Certainly not!*
Navigator: *There is no doubt about it-we're lost!*

JUST US $ 45,— WORTH OF FUEL, PLEASE.

Military flying is something. But luckily you are all alone in your cockpit and you are pestered only by voices on your radiochannels. But imagine having 350 passengers with you, who do things you don't like, or don't know about, or can't control. Now that's bad.

Once our squadron was airlifted to a remote destination by a reliable Fokker Friendship. Our friendship with the pilots did not last very long though. We started walking from the nose to tail and back as a group and the trim could not compensate fast enough for that. Can you imagine a Boeing 747 in which everybody goes to the toilet after a meal?

CAPTAIN, HE IS ASKING FOR A VECTOR TO MECCA

MICHAEL, PUT THAT BACK IMMEDIATELY

It is far better to be on the ground
wishing you were in the air.
Than to be in the air
wishing you were on the ground......

MAY I ASK YOU WHERE YOU LEARNED TO FLY ?

HE WHO TOUCHES PITCH WILL BE DEFILED

Snappy answers dept 6

Tower: *KLM 641, what's your height?*
Pilot: *My height is six feet two, without shoes.*

BASIC FLYING IS REGULARLY REINVENTED

DON'T BECOME A FOREIGN OBJECT

A flight of two F84F's was taking off somewhere back in the 50's. The name of one of the pilots was Henk. Minutes later they were disappearing in a dark cloud, flying close formation. In the mean time a second element of two aircraft was lining up on the runway. The name of one of the pilots was Henk. While Henk was revving up his engine at the threshold, his aircraft caught fire. The other pilot noticed this and gave an excited radio call: "Henk get out, you're on fire". Henk did not hesitate and made an emergency egress and started running. The other Henk, flying close formation, did not hesitate either and used his ejection seat to leave a perfectly serviceable aircraft, which crashed after flying pilotless for 10 more minutes.
This was a true story, and it might happen again!

WELL MY FRIEND IS SITTING TWO ROWS IN FRONT OF ME AND I JUST CALLED HIM: "HI JACK"

MY WIFE BERTHA INSISTED ON
KNITTING ONE FOR ME

NO, I DID NOT SAY : I HAVE CONTROL

Many people should know about "Fighter Pilots do it better",
but did you know about the next ones:

Young pilots do it eagerly
Old pilots do it with experience
Autopilots do it for you
Helicopter pilots do it with both hands
Glider pilots do it silently
Business jet pilots do it in luxury
Air defence pilots chase it
Copilots do it when their captains let them
Kamikaze pilots don't do it often
Jet pilots do it with more noise
Aerobatic pilots do it inverted
Agricultural pilots spill doing it
Ferry pilots do it longer
Instructor pilots pass it on
Instrument pilots do it without visual reference
Bomber pilots do it with a big bang
Student pilots sweat it out
Recce pilots peep at it
Russian pilots do it behind the curtain
Airline pilots do it in their shirtsleeves
Test pilots find new ways of doing it
Private pilots do it for fun
CIA pilots do it surreptitiously
Tanker pilots do it with long hoses
Without ECM nobody does it
Navigators do it more precisely
A-6 pilots do it all weather
Red Arrow pilots do it in style
Harrier pilots jump to it
Shackleton pilots do it for hours on end
Naval pilots get hooked doing it
Flight Safety Officers talk about it
Some pilots are written up for it
WX Recce pilots are never sure weather to do it
Australian pilots do it upside down
Controllers do it in the dark
Radar directors turn you on to it
Simulator pilots only pretend to do it
Hovercraft pilots do it in skirts
Company test pilots have first go at it
Carrier pilots do it with mirrors

In the struggle for customers for the F16 a large amount of information was distributed by the manufacturer. According to that the "Fighting Falcon" had some special qualities...

F 16 _ BORN TO BE A DOGFIGHTER

F 16 –
THE
FLASHING
FIGHTER

F 16 –
EXCELLENT
RIDING
QUALITIES

F 16 —
COMPUTERIZED
G-LIMITER

F 16 —
QUADRUPLE
REDUNDANCY

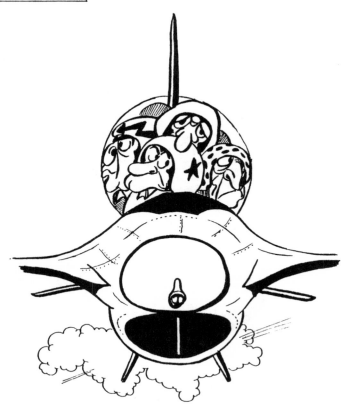

F 16 - MORE BANG FOR YOUR BUCK

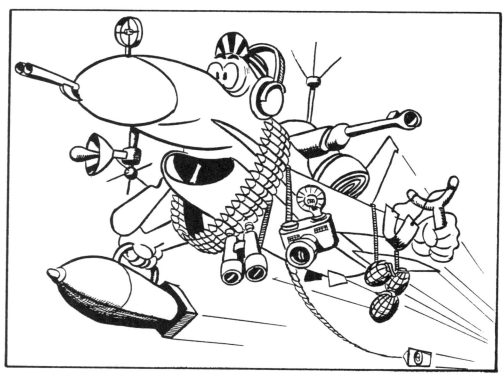

F 16 - MULTIROLE

F 16 - BUILT-IN SELF TEST

F 16 - AUTOMATIC ANGLE OF ATTACK LIMITER

Snappy answers dept 7

Pilot 1: *Let's make a 360 back home.*
Pilot 2: *Roger*

YOU REALLY ARE SOMEBODY IN THIS JOB

Every instructor will say it at least once to
every student: "Flying is so easy, I could learn
it to my grandmother, so why can't you make
a proper....etc...."
And it's true, if you can drive a car and if you
know your right hand from your left, you
should not have many problems learning how
to fly. But you might need a very good
instructor.

RRR-ONE, READY FOR LINE UP AND TAKE OFF

DO YOU THINK
YOU CAN HANDLE IT ?

Snappy answers dept 8

Tower: *You have traffic at 10 o'clock, six miles*
Pilot: *Give us another hint; we have digital watches*

EDDIE ALWAYS CHOOSES THE EASY WAY OUT

Snappy answers dept 9

Passenger: *How long takes a flight from Amsterdam to Copenhagen?*
Clerk: *One moment*
Passenger: *Thank you*

NO PHOTOGRAPHER ?

WHAT A RELIEF! I THOUGHT IT WAS A HARD LANDING

Control systems of aircraft have always been the same. A steering device, which can be a control stick, a yoke or anything like that, is connected with the control surfaces by (steel) rods or cables. The amount of displacement of the steering device regulates the amount of deflection of the control surface. Sometimes you need a hydraulic system for power to overcome the airloads in high-speed flying or heavy-weight aircraft, but the basic system has never been changed. Yet the fly-by-wire system is changing this old tradition. Steering commands are fed into a computer that decides what to give you and then sends electronic signals to the various flying controls for a deflection, or not.

Aircraft control systems of the eighties

FLY BY WIRE

Snappy answers dept 10

GCA: *Mission 1234, do you have problems?*
Pilot: *I think I have lost my compass.*
GCA: *Judging the way you are flying, it looks like you have lost the whole instrument panel.*

IT'S LIKE THE NAVY, ONLY YOUR RUNWAY IS WIDER

Snappy answers dept 11

Briefer: *During the airshow the minimum altitude for all partici- pants will be 300 feet, gentlemen.*
Pilot: *Roger, let's compare shoes. My feet are size 39 but your's look like 43 at least.*

This is what we call

Air Combat rules of engagement

1· *use as many tricks as possible*
2· *be unpredictable*
3· *use your common sense*
4· *WIN*

1

Snappy answers dept 12

Pilot: *Bierset tower, Green formation request permission for airfield attack?*
Tower: *Green, that's negative!*
Pilot: *Did you say negative?*
Tower: *Affirmative.*
Pilot: *Understand affirmative, I will call you leaving the zone.*

Due to the political structure of some EPG's (European Participating Governments) the facial expression of the F16 had to be changed,

from imperialistic complacency

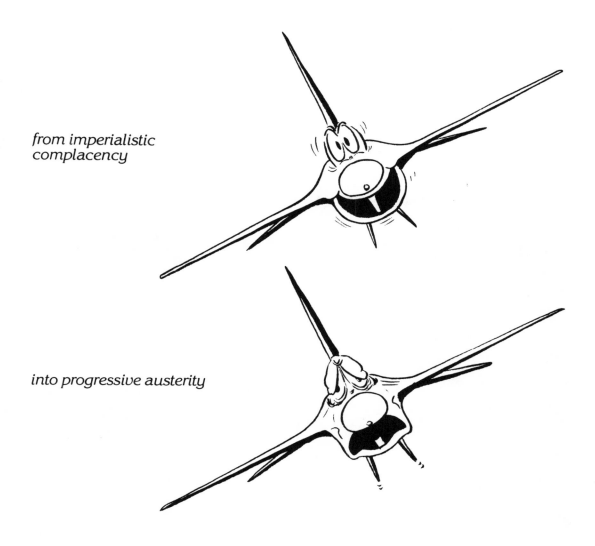

into progressive austerity

(which had no effect upon performance)

Snappy answers dept 13

Tower: *Redskin Green, the airfield is at your 2 o'clock position.*
Pilot: *Roger, is that local time or GMT?*

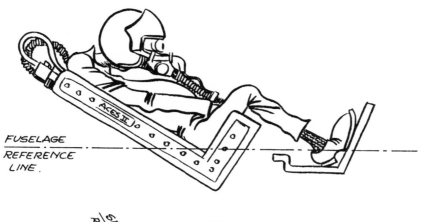

FUSELAGE REFERENCE LINE.

ACES II

SPINE REFERENCE LINE.

dorsal

The new high-G performance of the F16, a sustained 9G, made it necessary to change the seating position of the pilot. His chair is tilted backwards and the G-tolerance improves dramatically, the same happens with backaches.

Snappy answers dept 14

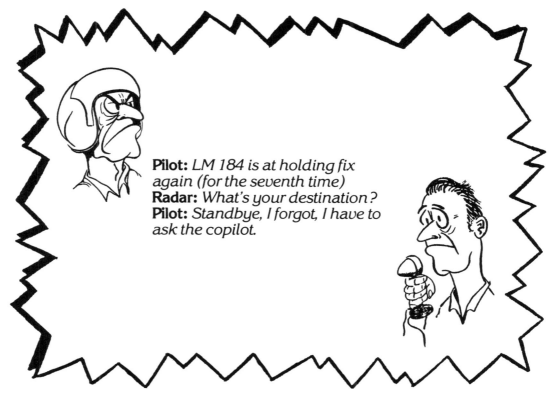

Pilot: *LM 184 is at holding fix again (for the seventh time)*
Radar: *What's your destination?*
Pilot: *Standbye, I forgot, I have to ask the copilot.*

The F16 modification program started before the construction program did.

The Dutch prefer the old-fashioned "stick-in-the-middle" position. That's where it always had been and nobody ever complained about it.

For presentation of navigation and fire control data, there were 3 options...

Snappy answers dept 15

Tower: *Mission 1234, you are cleared to... via... and via... After take-off.... and.... then...., climb to.... and further.... and descend.... Further instructions on frequency.... or.... and squawk.... Acknowledge please!*
Pilot: *Roger tower, we are cancelling IFR*

SOMEBODY CHANGED THE SOFTWARE

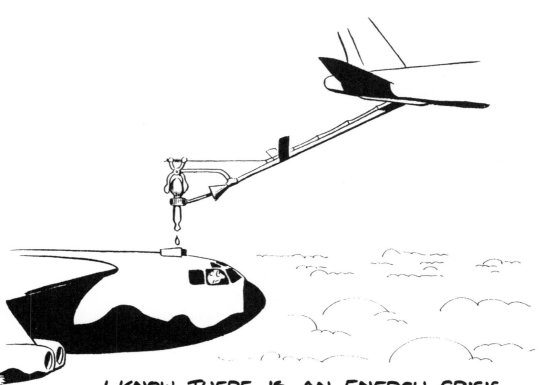

I KNOW THERE IS AN ENERGY CRISIS BUT THERE ARE LIMITS

Many things have been said about the relationship between pilots and navigators. And, like in a good marriage, many things have not been said. To the delight of navigators I have often told the story about the fighter pilot who was lost in northern Germany. He was calling radar stations on NATO combined frequencies, asking for vectors to anything. After a question of a radarcontroller he told him, and the rest of NATO, listening in, that he was flying a F4 Phantom. The Phantom carries a navigator..... After this story the Officer's Club will be roaring with laughter and discussions and jokes will continue the rest of the night.

It is hard to give a quick solution to this good-humoured rivalry, but if you ask an average fighter pilot, he will tell you that the main job of navigators and air traffic controllers is to confuse pilots.

YES, I AM QUITE SURE, THE AIRFIELD
MUST BE HERE

MISSION 118, WHERE ARE YOU?

The poor nice lady is in tears, just moments
ago she has wrecked her new car
against a tree. How can she ever explain this
to her husband, the pilot. In a nearby
phonebooth she phones him at the
squadron: "Darling, I have a small problem
with the car. It's something you would call
FOD".
FOD=Foreign Object Damage

YOU ARE THE ONLY PILOT I KNOW, WHO
COULD HIT A NON-FLYING BIRD

Electronic warfare is starting a life at its own. What began as a pilots aid against madmen shooting at them from the ground with the aid of electronic smart things is now a multimillion dollar industry. Clever scientists in huge laboratories are thinking about moves and countermoves like chess players. Against Electronic Measures came ECM (Electronic Counter Measures) which started off ECCM (EC Counter M). And so on. Recently they found a really good one: let the other side think you have a certain system, so that they start building their countermeasures; but in reality you don't have that system and don't even think about buying it. But then, that's becoming more or less a psychological warfare, and that's another story.

Electronic warfare

THERE IS ANOTHER 'SAM' AND I JUST RAN OUT OF FLARES

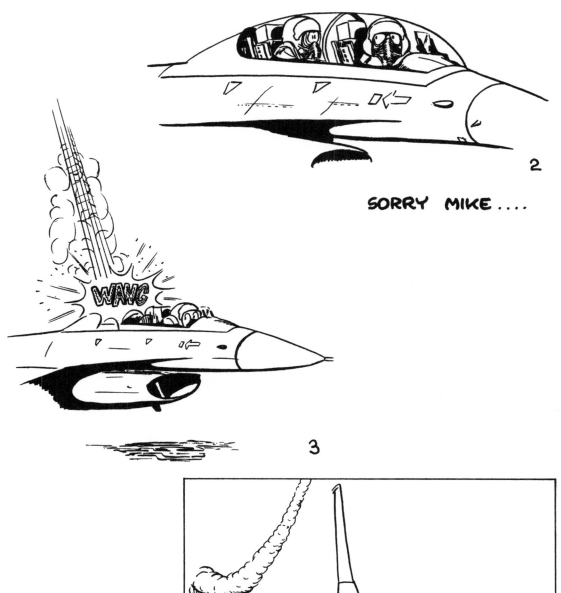

SORRY MIKE....

THAT'S BETTER

Snappy answers dept 16

Tower: *Paris tower to all aircraft, QNH is now 1017mb*
Pilot: *How come? Did everybody open their windows?*

THEY MADE SOME CALCULATIONS AND THIS
IS CHEAPER THAN WATCHDOGS

In a jet fighter there is always a need to "cover your six". In a normal two-ship formation you do that together and you will see almost every fighter sneaking in. But when you are flying a singleton navigation flight there is a real need for rubber-necked type of flying with many hard turns to watch the sky behind you. And if, while doing that, you hear a radiocall claiming a simulated "missile kill" on the common squadron frequency, it's time to start the most violent evasive actions you know. Because "every pilot is a tiger" and your squadron colleagues will talk about it for weeks when somebody claims you are "easy meat".

It is also very satisfying to know about all those evading fighters, just after you made the radiocall about the missile kill, while you are just taxiing an aircraft which needed a brake check......

This is what we call

VERTIGO

FIGHTER PILOTS BARTALK

Snappy answers dept 17

Range: *Did you drop a bomb on this run?*
Pilot: *Affirmative*
Range: *In that case, the score is "out of range"*

MY SIMPLE AND RELIABLE NAVIGATION SYSTEM,

WHEN THE SIGAR
IS FINISHED,
IT'S TIME
TO LAND

IF THE COFFEE LEAVES
THE CUP, YOU'RE
FLYING UPSIDE DOWN

In the old days, the job of an aircraft technician was different. Their work was simple: get the aircraft out of the hanger, fuel it and wipe off the oil, pull the propeller and remove the chocks, at the return of a flight the same in reverse order and when the aircraft does not work: repair it. The aircraft were simple and most jobs could be done by anybody.

Gradually their jobs changed with the complexity of the aircraft. It now takes crews of well trained men to keep an aircraft flying. Getting a military jet ready for flight is a multi-man job, and a small technical problem can keep these men busy for a long time. There are no more masters-of-all-trade and you have experts for every system. The hydraulics man knows nothing about armament or DC power or radar adjustment. So next to these experts the Air Force invented the man who has to coordinate who is working where on an aircraft: the crewchief. Every aircraft now has it's own crewchief and he is treating "his" aircraft like a mother treats her child. Sometimes you even have to be careful to tell a crewchief that his aircraft is unserviceable.

HE IS THE BEST CREWCHIEF WE EVER HAD

Snappy answers dept 18

Pilot: *Good morning, Frankfurt ground, KLM 242 request start up and push back, please.*
Ground: *KLM 242 expect start up in two hours.*
Pilot: *Please confirm, two hours delay?*
Ground: *Affirmative.*
Pilot: *In that case, cancel the good morning!*

THE PILOT SHOULD BE TREATED AS A KING

BUT HE NEEDS A HARD HEAD

The farmer who lives at the end of one of the Eindhoven Airbase runways is old and slowly getting deaf. All his life he has heard aircraft taking off and landing just over the top of the roof of his farm. You would expect him to be one of the most avid noise complainants. But he never complains. If you ask him whether the aircraft noise is unpleasant or not, you have to yell quite hard; he is really getting deaf. But than he will answer: "I like it better when they are noisy than when they are silent". He'll explain that a few years ago a noiseless aircraft made a crashlanding in his garden because of an engine failure. He likes noise better.

WHAT ? IT NEEDS A 10,000 FT RUNWAY ?

The thing is, helicopters are different from aeroplanes. An aeroplane wants to fly by it's nature, and if not interfered with too strongly by unusual events or by a deliberately incompetent pilot, it will fly. A helicopter does not want to fly. It is kept in the air by a variety of forces and controls working in opposition of eachother; and if there is any disturbance in the delicate balance, the helicopter stops flying immediately and disastrously. There is no thing as a gliding helicopter. This is why being a helicopter pilot is so different from being an aeroplane pilot and why, in general, aeroplane pilots are open, cleareyed, buoyant extroverts, and helicopter pilots are brooders, introspective anticipators of trouble. They know if anyting bad has not happened, it is about to......

HMMM.... QUITE A BIT OF GRAVITY HERE

This is what we call

A HIGH TENSION INCIDENT

Snappy answers dept 19

Tower: *Aircraft on final, overshoot, overshoot, your gear is up!*
Pilot: *Tower, can you say again, this horn is making such a noise.*

This is what we call

THE FLIGHT AFTER THE NIGHT BEFORE

A BIRDSTRIKE

Flight Safety Officers are generally old and wise pilots. Their job is to improve flying safety and, in short, their message is: "Be wise and get old". But sometimes it is hard to get this message into the minds of young and bold pilots. And even the FSO has to agree that he also got wise by the years.

OUR FLIGHT SAFETY OFFICER IS TRYING NEW
METHODS TO REACH THE YOUNG PILOTS

Sometimes it takes almost nothing to get a passenger vomitingly sick. The smallest bump or the easiest turn or just the idea of flying will cause him to be sick just behind your back. But it can be a problem to get passengers you dislike, sick on purpose. Some arrogant or big-mouthed people are just asking to be transformed into a pitiful heap of sick human being. They may have solid-steel stomachs but some unexpected negative G or improvised variants on your (sloppy) aerobatic program will get them sick eventually (it might even get your own stomach turning).

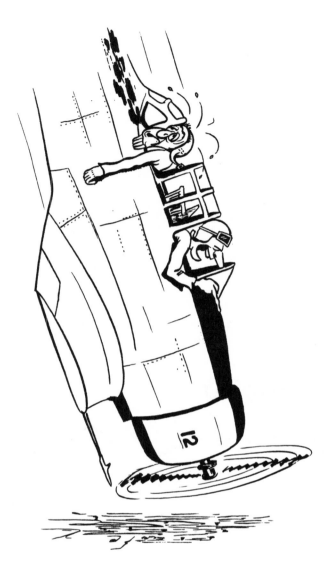

LOOK, THERE IS THAT
RESTAURANT WHERE
THEY SERVE THOSE
EXCELLENT SNAILS

Snappy answers dept 20

Tower: *PH-ABC, check you have the gear down?*
Pilot: *Sir, it has been down since the aircraft was built.*

LADIES AND GENTLEMEN, I HOPE YOU WILL
UNDERSTAND THAT THIS IS NOT PART OF
OUR STANDARD ENTERTAINMENT PROGRAM

It always pays to be friendly with your technical personnel. If you do, you will get a better aircraft sooner and with less problems. Because if they don't like you, there are ways to show you just that. You will always get the aircraft with the worn tires, crewchief who just went to the dentist, last minute write-ups, dirty windows, overheated cockpit because it has been standing in the sun for 3 hours, suspected landinggear problems or anything worse than that. Eventually this machine they assigned to you will fly, but most probably with someone else.

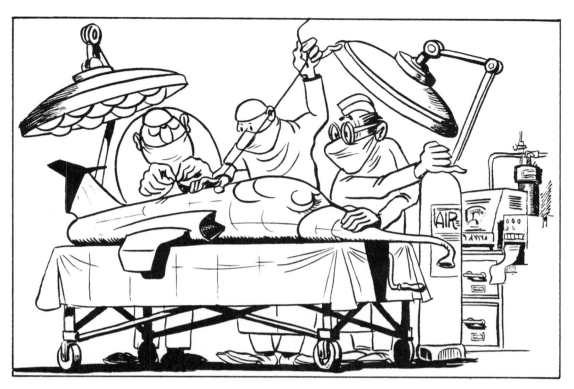

MAINTENANCE IS A DELICATE ART

BUT SOMETIMES YOU NEED INFLIGHT REPAIRS

A student pilot had to make a solo flight with a T6 Harvard. There were rows and rows of aircraft on the flightline but only two had had a recent modification. A different type of propeller was fitted which was about two inches longer than usual. You had to look hard to see it. The student got one of these two aircrafts assigned to him and managed to hit the ground with the propellertip during unauthorized low flying. When he reported the tipdamage to his flight commander he added that he had not been flying lower than usual and that he had hit the ground due to this long propeller.... Everybody was so astonished at this kind of argumentation that he even could continue his flying training.

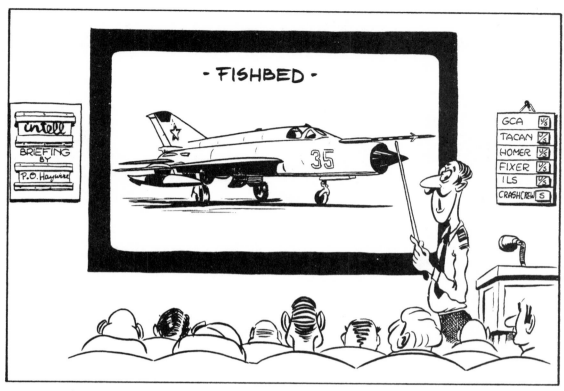

RED AND WHITE STICK IN FRONT;
WE SUPPOSE IT IS FIT FOR BLINDFLYING

LOW FLYING? NO SIR, NOT LOWER THAN USUAL

In some airlines, the boss is not a pilot, but an accountant. It's not that bad yet in the Air Force but even there bosses are fighting a downhill battle against these human calculators. A pilot's job is flying, and in between flights he is drinking coffee. At least that's how it was, nowadays a squadron pilot has secundary duties next to his flying job. These duties quite often take so much time he even has to skip flights for them. This way the Air Force cuts down expenses twofold: they need less people and the pilots make less (expensive) flying hours.

OOPS!

A landing on a wet runway should be of the firm kind, to avoid aquaplaning. So it says in the big book. Sometimes a captain has to tell this tale to his passengers using the public address system to explain a rather solid arrival. But if he does so when the sun is shining and the runway is nice and dry, start thinking about booking on other airlines.

DID WE LAND OR WERE WE SHOT DOWN ?

Evolution in weapon systems

A dumb bomb is not as dumb as it looks. It is as smart as the smart guy who drops his dumb bomb smack on target. The smart bomb degrades in the hands of a dumb operator to a very dumb weapon.

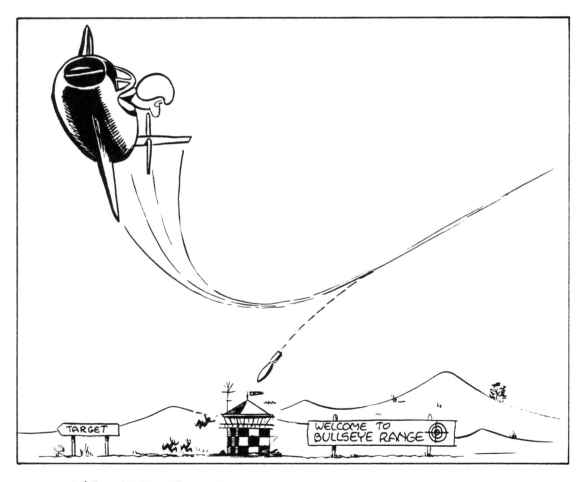

WE USED TO USE DUMB BOMBS.....

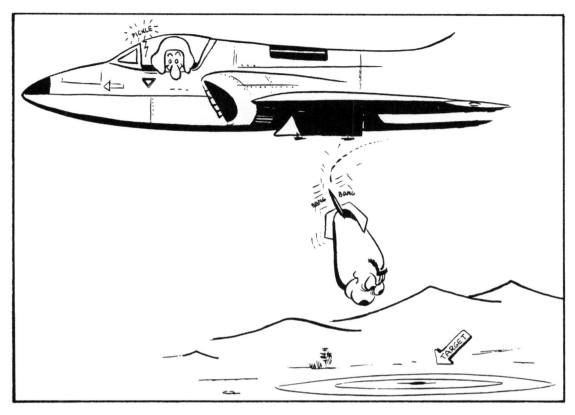

... NOWADAYS WE HAVE SMART WEAPONS,.....

...BUT THE DAY
WILL COME WHEN
WEAPONS ARE
SMARTER
THAN PILOTS !

A student pilot has to face two problems. The first is the aeroplane, a devilish piece of machinery that resists all attempts to control the direction of movement. A solution can be found though in a mixture of perseverance, practice, curses, cool knowledge and an occasional kick. The second problem, the flight instructor, is not so easily solved. The instructor is a special breed of pilot. He is easily recognizable by his great courage, extreme skill, low forehead, and mean little eyes. But because the instructor already knows how to fly, he has the student completely at a disadvantage. He is unimpressed with whatever skills the student might have outside of aviation.

Therefore, he is dedicated to showing the student how little he knows and, by his own example, how completely unsuitable the student is as pilot material. Those who wish to make a success of flying are advised to follow a few simple rules in their dealing with instructors:

1- the instructor is always right.
2- when the instructor is wrong, it should be avoided to tell him so in public, unless he is testing you!
3- try to find in the books what is really right; use it to teach yourself in solo flying.
4- keep on doing stupid things during your flying lessons; instructors prefer to think all students never learn.

WE ARE GOING TO SHARE A LITTLE SECRET

YOUR FLYING UNTIL NOW
WAS NO SUCCES;
I HOPE YOU DON'T
MESS UP YOUR
LANDING AS WELL

Murphy's Law

If anything can go wrong, it will.

This is the original Law of Murphy which
has some derivations:
● If there is a possibility of several things
going wrong, the one that will cost most to
repair will be the one to go wrong.
● If you anticipate three different ways in
which a procedure can go wrong, and
circumvent these, then a fourth way will
promptly develop.
● Every solution brings about new
problems.
● No matter what goes wrong, it will
probably look right.
Industry has been working for years now to
out-manoeuvre Murphy but it looks like a
lost cause. It is virtually impossible to keep
ahead of Murphy; and remember his
philosophy:
● Smile, tomorrow will be worse....

CALLS US
FIXED WINGERS

MY NAME IS MURPHY

In just a few years aviation developed into an industry which the modern world needs. In the beginning of the century it were just hops on a grassfield but now you can fly at Mach 2 in a Concorde. Aircraft like the Jumbo fly routinely with take off weights of more than 500 tons. But a few things never change:
● An aircraft from the right has right of way.
● A powerless aircraft has right of way from a powered aircraft.
● An aircraft in the landing phase has right of way from a cruising aircraft.

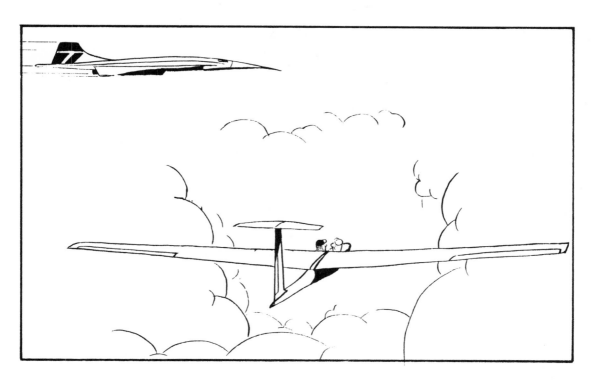

NOT TO WORRY, WE HAVE RIGHT OF WAY

Intentionally
left
blank

Acknowledgements

Just writing a book must be easy, you talk into a taperecorder and bring the tape to a publisher who takes care of the rest and sends you a monthly cheque. We did not do it that way. This book is real private enterprise and everything, drawing, writing, typing, designing and marketing, was done by ourselves. There were some small problems every now and then, buth with some help we solved them.

We like to thank Annie and Cornélie for getting through those long and dull evenings without complaining and even urging us to continue.

We like to thank Rein van Beeck and his staff for printing the first edition.

We like to thank De Groot printers in Goudriaan for printing all other editions after the first one.

We like to thank Bert Buitenberg for correcting the grammatical mistakes.

We like to thank the photographic section of Eindhoven Airbase for the cover picture.

We like to thank everybody in the Netherlands Air Force for doing what they have done to give us those funny ideas.

We like to thank all NATO and civilian pilots for all those strong stories at the bar.